RISE UP AND WALK

RISE UP AND WALK

BY

TURNLEY WALKER

1950

E. P. DUTTON & CO., INC.

PUBLISHERS   NEW YORK

A Story Press Book

From the series of articles "I Am a Polio"
syndicated by the North American Newspaper Alliance

CONTENTS

I

Polio Is a Lonely Place

THE REGULATION HOSPITAL BED is thirty-four by seventy-four inches. In the beginning that much space is allotted to each *polio*—the new name you get after Infantile Paralysis slugs you. Forever after you will be known as *a polio*. That thirty-four-by-seventy-four inch area is a place that poliomyelitis allows you, and even though you have been a much-traveled man in the outside world, you learn to live in it.

At first it's a very quiet life. You lie flat on your back, stretched out as far as you will go, and nothing about you moves—if you are a serious case—except the wheels inside your head. Those wheels grind out a terrible pressure of fear and pain and loneliness. Very suddenly, you have been yanked out of the relaxed, marvelous, commonplace world and set down in a tiny flat white jail. Polio is always so unexpected.

Your hospital, the Hospital for Special Surgery, is a fine one. It stands between First and Second Avenues on Forty-second Street in Manhattan—and on the shore of the East River just a block away, big things are happening. The cornerstone of the permanent

United Nations Headquarters is being laid by a number of very important men.

You painfully twist your head upon the inch-high pillow, and a square foot of blue sky is visible through the window-top. You stare at this, listening to the oratorical voice of one of the earth's great men which seems to come from it. The public address system of the United Nations has been tuned very loud, a surprising sort of boldness. The voice is impassioned and heavy with the weight of self-conscious statesmanship. You examine your patch of blue sky and are remarkably unimpressed. This world which is discussed so foolishly is a million miles away.

There is a rumor, running swift as ground lightning through the ward, that President Truman will come directly from the dedication ceremonies to see the *polios* in your hospital, to call upon *you*. To drop in for a friendly, man-to-man chat. The information makes you smile. You see a kind of humor in it. And you are not disappointed when the President goes directly to the Mayor's house instead. There used to be a President who knew something about polio, but he is no longer with us.

Your left big toe has gone numb again, and this is truly important. You yank a cord to turn on a signal light in the corridor, you storm with impatience for thirty seconds, and then, as suddenly, you are ashamed enough to weep. You cannot move to bring aid to your

big toe, and this is a defeat overwhelming in its humil-
iation. Your total life has narrowed to the dimensions
of your bed.

You watch the blue fade from your patch of sky, and
long for hunger because you know the supper hour is
upon you. But, in the beginning, appetite is not allowed
a *polio*. He is packed too full of pain and fear. If he
disturbs himself with so much as a deep breath, his
whole body pushes in rage against his throat.

Your hospital bed is your only place in the world,
and in polio's first stages you resent all advances across
its borders. Any handling of your useless body enrages
you. Your loneliness is all you have, and you can force
some strange small satisfactions from it, if you are not
bothered.

By the time visitors begin to arrive, there is darkness
all around, and a nurse lights the reading lamp which
twists out on a limber neck from the headboard of your
bed. The groans of a patient in the nearest bed are
entirely understandable, and soothing as well. Another
country is heard from, a country in which you would
not be a stranger. Your heart does not ache for the tor-
ture of this other bed-clasped life. Your heart has
melted through your own unmoving body, and its pity
will not reach elsewhere.

You begin to force up your courage to meet your
wife's eyes. You hear her quick footsteps. Her watchful face moves towards you like a smooth full pressure

of love, and by the wetness of your cheeks you know that you are crying.

That's what polio is like in the beginning.

Right after it hits you like a hammer in the head.

II

A Friend a Long Way Off

You SPEND a considerable part of your time estimating small but important distances. By the hour, you stare at the open doorway of your room. Somehow, someday, you must walk to that doorway from the faraway pit of helplessness in which you lie.

Between your bed and the next there is a gleaming space of dark brown linoleum which seems to your eye just about six feet, not so wide as you were tall when you were capable of standing upright, but now become a tremendous void over which you have no control. At the ends of your lifeless legs, your feet are pinned flat against an upright board to prevent their twisting in the disease's painful spasms, and movement across a floor is a forgotten miracle.

On the other bed a man lies full length on his back. The day before you watched them roll him into the room and turn him from the stretcher into this permanent position. Their hands touched him tenderly, but he screamed in rage, and under your breath, you cursed their hands in his behalf. You did not know his name,

11

you had not seen his face because a high table cut it off from view, but he was a friend of yours. He groaned and called out for the nurses in an exasperated voice. He was afraid. To the depths of your soul, you understood him.

Now you watch his bare feet in their tight position on the footboard. Can he move them? You watch him try. You feel the terrific straining of his body, but the feet remain indifferent. It gives a certain satisfaction that he holds no advantage over you, and that all distances beyond the white shelf of his bed are as meaningless for him.

Then suddenly you feel a longing to be close to him, perhaps to take his hand with your one hand which has retained its normal strength, and to examine with him the pit into which you both have fallen. But the distance of the floor lies there between you, as wide as the Atlantic, and he has twisted his shoulder towards the other wall, moaning to himself. He might be your first friend in this new world of polio, but he is so far away.

An activity of nurses and attendants sets up between your beds. They are giving him his hot packs, the nearly boiling water gurgling from the wringer of the old-fashioned washing machine, the thick chunks of blanket steaming in the tongs as they are carried to his naked, fearful body, and he snarls at the sharp discomfort before the soothing effect comes. He is a long way off, and your world and his are disconnected.

You fight your way over onto the side which sets your face towards your own private wall and fall to examining once again the completeness of the disaster which polio has brought.

In that lost outside world you were a man who counseled business executives upon methods they might use to explain their activities to their employees and the public. A label for this work has come to common usage: public relations; and you were a partner in a small concern which sold this specialty.

In addition, over the past two years, a desire to write fiction pressed up inside you, almost unexpectedly, and you worked on this at night; night after night, month after month. On the advice of a friend, you mailed a scrap of writing to a distinguished editor and publisher who with his wife had a unique reputation for discovering new writers of value. These people totally surprised you by buying the story and telling you that you had the talent to write a novel around the same characters and situations. In three months' time you wrote such a manuscript, and the editor secured a contract on it with one of the large publishing houses.

But now your brain wallows in a delirium of fear and pain, and the required rewriting seems a permanent impossibility. And you can no longer carry your body and mind into the offices of businessmen to counsel them. Lying in your bed, you cannot remember where you left the book manuscript, and this loss of control over precious possessions terrifies you. And you know your business cannot be saved.

The distance between your shoulders and the wall is about eighteen inches, but your weakened hand cannot reach it. You feel that if you could reach the wall and beat upon it with your fist, your anguish might be relieved. You lie there, sweating, until weakness begins to creep through you everywhere, and you doze.

An attendant's hands turn you over on your back once more and jam your will-less feet against the board. You are lifted this way and that to receive the burning hot packs. And then, the spasms soothed, you sleep.

When they remove the packs, you come wide awake again, with the thought riveted in your mind that your family will soon have no money to live on. An overpowering worry is presented by the costs of the hospital and your treatments. In a very short time, the hospital payment plan to which you have subscribed for years will become meaningless. The medical equipment and attention which surround you indicate the terrific expense of polio, and this may continue for many months. Your mind begins its familiar rage at the trap in which you have been caught.

You look across the distance to the inert body on the neighboring bed. It's a joke, a lousy joke, to think that there might be an exchange of help between you. You are sinking steadily, and there is no support beneath you anywhere. You are busy at the crime of creating terrific expenses while helpless to provide income for your dependents.

Certainly the general situation would be improved if polio should take you down out of consciousness, as it did in the first few days of its attack, and this time leave you there.

But this mood does not hold, because the visiting period comes 'round, and your wife appears carrying a miracle in the shape of a brisk white business envelope.

She reads it to you, and gratefulness at what it says makes you weep together. There is an organization called the National Foundation for Infantile Paralysis. . . . Oh yes, you had heard of it . . . something called the March of Dimes to which you gave a few dollars every year . . . but the important aspects of it had escaped your attention.

The letter says that you are not to worry if you do not have the money to pay for your treatments. The letter says that the National Foundation for Infantile Paralysis will stand behind you, taking care of all your medical and hospital expenses if need be, until you are able to go to work again.

Until you are able to work again, the letter says. It lets you *know* that you are not lost forever, but only out of circulation for a while because of a dreadful accident.

You try to think over this remarkable attitude carefully, but the tears keep coming.

"I never heard of anything like it," your wife says several times.

"You mean I don't have to worry?" you ask cautiously at last.

She assures you by smiles and by clutching your tired shoulders.

After she is gone, you can still see her smiling, and you see that the letter means precisely what it says. This *Foundation* has suddenly become a personal and powerful friend of yours. Down underneath you somewhere a support has risen. You can almost feel it with your feet. It is almost like feeling a floor with feet that suddenly can move again.

It is night, and the lamps are lighted on the heads of the beds, four of them around the room. The dark brown linoleum gleams warmly, and now the distance between your bed and the next seems narrower.

"Hello there," you call out very carefully.

The other body wrenches towards you, comes up on its side, and you know the unseen face is turned in your direction.

"Hello," your new friend says.

His voice sounds close enough, and perhaps your voice is the same to him. You turn on your side toward him. At the strained movement, spasms of pain jerk upward along your spine, but then you feel better than you have for days. He is listening for you, waiting for you, and you know that the distance between your beds has vanished.

III

New World Alive with Strange Activities

YOUR NEW FRIEND in the bed six feet away is having another crying spell. You lie there thinking how strange it is for a thirty-seven-year-old lawyer to be sobbing in his bed at dawn.

You know why he is crying, of course. It is because his legs are paralyzed. He has been thinking about some situation in which his legs have given him great pleasure—perhaps a softball game, or simply running with his ten-year-old boy—and then the tears began to come.

You hear him fighting for control, and you wait until he has gained this small victory. Then you yawn noisily.

He listens in your direction.

"Good morning," he says to you.

"I had a lousy sleep," you tell him.

"Me, too," he says.

"I had to call the night nurse a dozen times to move me."

"I know."

"I was aching everywhere, but they wouldn't give me more dope after twelve o'clock."

"I was listening," he tells you.

"You didn't sleep, then."

"I never sleep," he says.

"Dope complicates nerve recovery," you say. "A nurse told me."

"These nurses know everything."

"You don't like them?"

"They want to help, but I wish they'd leave me alone," says your new friend. "I don't like women pulling me around. When I go numb at night, and they move me, I never look at them. I pretend I'm doing it myself."

You nod in agreement. The high tables are between you, and you still have not seen his face.

Your friend lies quiet for several minutes, and then you hear his breathing begin to catch in his throat. He is thinking of how much he lost when his legs went dead.

Fortunately, the first nurse of the day comes trotting into the room.

"Here comes one of our friends," you tell him.

"The pretty one," he answers.

You eye the rawboned woman, gray hair, rimless glasses, a pinched-in, tired mouth.

"Right as rain," you say.

She hears these comments, and smiles.

"You boys seem to be feeling better," she says.

She comes to your bed and begins to arrange your

body for the difficult business of eating breakfast lying on your side. Her face is kind, and you know that her skilled hands are as gentle as she can make them, but each time she touches the spasm-tightened muscles you wince, and you hate her as someone who outrages your sickened body.

Across the way, your new friend suddenly snarls, "Don't touch my leg that way . . . please . . . !" The nurse attending him is small and rather good-looking, but this brings no relief. All such people invade the shelter of your bed and so are enemies.

Lying propped upon your weak right shoulder you begin handling the food methodically. You are not hungry, but you know you must eat. You now weigh 166, which means that you have lost fifty pounds. The boiled egg tastes like sawdust and it is hard to swallow.

The effort of lifting your arm again and again in eating tires you so that you sweat profusely, the strained position makes you ache in unusual places, and when at last you are finished, you long to be absolutely quiet so that perhaps you may slip deep into sleep again.

But, throughout the room, the strange activities of your treatment have begun to swirl.

The machinery for the hot packs is rushed up to your friend's bed, and you are rolled onto a stretcher while your own bed is made. Back in the bed again, cursing at the handling of your body, a young woman, truly good-looking this time, appears and begins an examination of your muscles. She wants to know how much power is left and just where it is located. She hauls and tugs, and orders you to make certain movements. None of them is possible, and you glare at her in exasperation.

She smiles and pats one of your inert legs.

"I wouldn't worry," she tells you briskly. "There's a lot of strength in you. In you somewhere. We'll find it."

You shut your eyes and try to do exactly as she tells you. She asks you to make a certain movement, and you drive the thought of it with all your might down from your mind toward the lifeless leg. But the thought doesn't get there. Some deadly barrier lies between.

"All right, once more," she says.

You could kill her for her bright self-confidence, and are glad when she is through. Around you in the room the weird activities whirl, washing over your bed from time to time. Your legs and back are stretched by two strong young men. Agony. You are rolled again to a stretcher and hurled down a hallway, through a door and dumped into a hot-water tank. It nearly suffocates you, but the effect is soothing. Just when you relax, however, the overhead crane creaks you up to the stretcher again, and you are off on the return journey.

At every shifting of your body you are terribly frightened. Terror that you will be dropped, or fall, makes you clutch wildly with your sound hand. In your own bed again and sweating under two thick blankets, you pray that no new attack will follow.

But around you through the room, the vigorous activities continue. The blankets are yanked away, and you are bathed. The hot-pack machinery is rushed in your direction. You are learning that no *polio* is treated like a sick man. Doctors have discovered that weakened muscles, and those apparently dead, must be kept *alive*. They work like stokers in a coalhole, and your pain-wracked body is lifted, turned, packed, dried, tested, exercised. Their activities keep you spinning in a whirl-pool, and you hate them all.

At last a respite comes, and your thoughts turn at once upon your new friend.

"How goes it?" you call out.

"They say I'm living, but I'm not convinced," he answers.

You like his voice. It makes you smile. You turn over on your side facing him, and his own body strains up to a position facing you. A nurse comes by, and you ask her to move the two tall tables so that you can see your friend's face. She does this cheerfully.

Your friend has dark crinkled hair and a big-boned fearless kind of face. From the sideways position, his eyes stare levelly into yours.

His neck is thick and one big shoulder hunches up

high. Your liking for him catches you inside, and you don't know what to say.

"Hi there, friend," he says with the grim, tender tone you have come to know.

"Great little vacation spot," you tell him.

"Lovely," he replies.

You like the way he grins, and you grin back. The loneliness fades out as you watch each other.

IV

Examining Your Doctor

AT FIRST doctors mean little to you. Your room has four beds, four narrow white cells in the jailhouse of the ward into which you have been locked, and the white-clad people who swarm through it are nurses, attendants, physiotherapists. A doctor makes his rounds night and morning, but he is not *the* doctor, not the celebrated specialist. You wonder about this man, and ask questions.

You are still pain-wracked and for long stretches of the day and night your mind holds nothing but your own very personal fears and the anguished, awesome realization that you cannot move your legs.

But during the shorter intervals when your mind widens to the general situation, you think about your doctor who is coming soon, and a conversation concerning him picks up around the room.

"I hear he came from Sweden years ago," you say.

Your special friend, the lawyer, twists up on his side to face you.

"I wouldn't be surprised," he says. "Sweden's where

they invented most of this stuff we're getting; hot packs, muscle re-education, all of that."

"What about the National Foundation?" asks a huge, hairy-chested man from a bed twelve feet down the room. He is a new patient, and you are just beginning to know him. All night long he groans at the pain which gnaws away inside his neck and head. For almost a week they thought that he might die. At thirty-two, he heads a concern that manufactures ladies' underwear, panties to be exact, and when polio first got him he weighed nearly 250 pounds. You and your lawyer friend have not quite accepted him yet, and you hesitate before answering.

You like him for bringing the National Foundation for Infantile Paralysis into the conversation.

The lawyer says: "Okay, the National Foundation and the Swedes.

Again there is a moment of waiting, in case the occupant of the remaining bed should want to make a statement. But he is listening. He is just eighteen years old, and very lightly hit. The suffering which he has observed in the beds around him has engendered deep respect.

"My wife went to the Foundation," says the pantie manufacturer, "and they told her our doctor is as good as anybody in the world."

"I'll go along, then," says the lawyer.

It is strange and interesting how completely the Foundation has become the final authority for all of you. You have come to know that it is your great ally in your fight, stronger than the hospital, as wise as all the doctors.

"My father is a doctor," you tell them, "and he knows about this man clear out in the State of Washington where I used to live."

"I'd like to *see* the guy," says the pantie manufacturer.

"I heard he might come tomorrow," says the lawyer.

"You hear that every other day," says the pantie manufacturer.

There is a time of silence while you each go over your private collection of rumors concerning the arrival of the great physician.

"I'd like to talk to him about my legs," says the lawyer.

"Legs?" says the pantie manufacturer. "Everything."

"How bad are you?" you ask.

"Man, I'm paralyzed. This hand wiggles a little, the rest of me is like I'm dead."

"What do you expect, a magician?" demands the lawyer.

"Why not?" the pantie manufacturer muses. "You never can tell."

Quiet settles down again, as you ponder the possibility that this unusual man will call life back into your deadened limbs almost immediately. You know this is a silly line of thought, but there is comfort in it.

A day passes and another, and then the hall outside your room is suddenly astir with a new kind of activity. The *word* rushes in and touches each of the beds. The eighteen-year-old boy sits up, he alone able to manage such an enormous movement.

"He's here!" he shouts.

"We know, we know . . ." the pantie manufacturer murmurs.

You lie tense in your flat position on the bed.

Nurses, therapists, an attendant or two press through the doorway. Other doctors form an anxious inward-turning circle. And then you see him. He is not an old man, but his hair is white. Near the center of the room he stands rather stiffly, and the others clear a space behind him so that he can look around. His eyes touch yours, blue eyes glancing with cool pleasantness.

"Good afternoon," he says.

You nod. His eyes travel to the other beds, and your friends make what slight gestures they can. You envy the teen-age boy the great advantage of his sitting position.

The doctor goes first to this boy's bed. He murmurs something pleasant, and you see the boy's wide grin. The doctor's careful hands go touching over him. You can see very little of this, and you speculate diligently. Next the pantie manufacturer is visited. A longer time is taken, but all is screened from you by the crowd of professional lookers-on. Next comes your special friend, the lawyer. Again you can see nothing.

The crowd breaks open, and the doctor approaches your bed with his stiff but steady stride. He puts his hands on the edge of the bed, and peers into your eyes.

"How are you feeling?" he asks.

"All right," you say.

He glances at the card at the head of the bed which gives your name and the date of the onset of the disease.

"It's still too early to tell much about you," he says.

"I can't move much of anything," you tell him. "Just this arm . . . this way."

He watches the small struggle you make.

"We'll see," he says.

He lifts up the blanket and peers down at your naked, lifeless legs. You feel his fingers catch you just above the knee, first one leg, then the other.

"Clench the muscle," he tells you.

You try with all your might. In the left leg nothing happens, but in the right something does. A thrill tears through you. "I can *feel* . . ." you stammer, daring not to hope.

"Yes, it's there," he says.

"You mean, my leg . . . ?"

"A very important muscle."

"Will it make me walk?"

"We'll watch it," he says.

He straightens up. He is going away. There are a thousand things you must know! But when his cool blue eyes hold yours, you cannot speak.

"We'll see," he says. His hand touches you gently on the shoulder. He smiles for an instant. His quiet fingers reassure you. And then he is gone.

The room clears quickly. It is very quiet. You and your friends are quiet on your beds, all but the boy who is still sitting up, his eyes turning solemnly this way and that.

"He didn't say much," says the pantie manufacturer at last, "but I got a kind of feeling. . . ."

"I like that guy, I really like him," says the lawyer softly.

You reach up your good hand and touch the place on your shoulder where the doctor's fingers rested.

"He found a muscle in my right leg," you tell them.

There is an atmosphere in the room now, of courage and a peculiar kind of confidence.

V

You Are Watching Other Faces . . .
Other Faces Watching You

THE SOCIAL-SERVICE WORKER for the hospital stands by
your bed. She is a stocky, neatly constructed woman
with iron-gray hair and a flushed, good-natured face.
You will come to admire her intelligence and energy,
and to understand that she is the hospital's necessary
connecting link with the local chapter of the National
Foundation for Infantile Paralysis.

Now she is only a pleasant voice and smile attached
to a trim physician's coat. She has a book for you.

"You've been asking everybody for information about
polio," she says.

"As long as I have it, I'd like to understand."

Here is a book that you will want to see; it was pub-
lished last year.

She hands it to you, and you read the title, *Polio and
Its Problems*.

You look up and find that she is watching you.

"Is everything all right?" she asks. "I mean, in the
outside world, with your family?"

"I don't know yet. Things are in a jumble with my business."

"The Foundation is worried about you. They'll help in any way they can."

"That's very nice. . . ." You continue to wonder at the generosity of this amazing organization.

"Meanwhile, the book ought to answer some of your questions," she says and leaves your bedside.

You glance through the book, riffling the pages. You like books. It has been a long time since you were calm enough to read one, and this book is nicely printed, well constructed. You turn to where the written material begins.

"So you've got a book about polio," says your special friend, the lawyer.

"Yes."

Around the room, other faces are watching yours. The teen-age boy, so lightly hit by the disease, is in his sitting position. You can see the broad quiet face of the pantie manufacturer in a lifted strained position, eyeing you over the footboard of his bed.

"Maybe you could read a little bit of it out loud," he says.

"That's what I mean," the lawyer says.

"Okay," you tell them.

You begin to read, intending to skip along the highlights. But the book holds your attention, line by line.

You are reading about the last of the great contagious killers. For you, polio is no longer simply the strange numbness which grips your legs but a coolly insane murderer crawling through your neighborhood with sub-microsocopic stealth. The pages roll away beneath your eyes. You glance up, and see the other faces riveted upon your own.

"What a stinking, lousy thing it is," mutters the pantie manufacturer. "And they don't know how it works—where it goes—they can't even *see* it."

"They'll find all that out, though, someday," says the lawyer. "Research takes years, they try everything, and then all of a sudden one day, wham! they've got it."

"It got me first," says the pantie manufacturer.

You look into each other's faces.

The pantie manufacturer makes his one small gesture, a slight, unsteady wave of his right hand.

"Thank God, though, it didn't get my kids. I'd rather have it five times over than have one of them turned into a cripple."

The three of you who have children nod quietly at each other. The teen-age boy stares out into the room.

"So go ahead," says the pantie manufacturer, "read some more."

The pages turn. Other faces are watching yours. You read until suppertime, and then after that hour, pick up the book again, to continue until the night nurse turns the lights out. Much of the book remains, but already you are reaching some understanding of the terrifying virus which has hidden all secrets of its own contagion, which slithers its way into the brains and spinal cords of children and grown men by pathways not yet discovered, and kills or cripples according to its whims.

Scarcely a century ago there was smallpox, typhus, diphtheria, the other plagues which carried death. But the human brains they sought to fry with fever outthought them all. Controls were found. And polio became the sole deadly epidemic menace still at large.

With perfect freedom polio makes its choice of people, not killing everybody it strikes, only eight or ten per cent; not crippling its whole selection; but *free to act* as it pleases. People can make no bargain with it. There is no preventive, and no cure.

In the darkness of your hospital room, other faces are turned towards your own. You are watching other faces.

"I came in from work one night," says the pantie manufacturer. "I felt sort of funny, like I was getting a cold. My back ached me some. And a couple of days later, I couldn't move."

You listen to him.

"I was a strong guy," he says. "I never had a sick day in my life."

You are thinking about the pleasant summer night you felt your brains begin to scramble slightly, as if with fatigue. And this seemed to be the case, since you had been working long hours on your book. Then your back began to break with pain, and after a day and night, your leg caved way beneath you on your way across the living room.

"I was fishing at Lake George with my older boy," the lawyer says. "My neck got stiff, then all of a sudden I couldn't walk. I had to hire a man to drive us back to the city in my car. And in Albany he sideswiped a truck, and I couldn't even get up from the back seat to argue."

Your faces are all lost in the darkness of the room, but you are watching each other carefully.

"The Foundation is trying to find how to kill off the lousy thing," says the pantie manufacturer.

"They will, someday," comes the lawyer's quiet voice.

"In the meantime, I'm in great shape," says the pantie manufacturer.

You laugh at him. You have come to like him very much.

You are quiet for a time. Night has settled down thickly now, the long, long night that holds sleeplessness and the worst of your pain. You try to cling to the feeling of your laughter, but the fears and the despair come creeping back. Your legs won't move. In the outside world, *what will you do?* People walk and run and step high and skip downstairs. And people stare at cripples, giving them wide clearance.

Faces are watching out into the room.

"We were laughing a minute ago," the lawyer says.

"That's because we're safe right now, lying on these beds. We'll have to leave these beds someday." You hear his voice catch in his throat. "God, I'm scared."

Each of you is watching for a glimpse of other faces, seeking some sign of hope and courage, but the night has settled down too thick for eyes to see.

VI

The Wives Come Trooping In

FOR A TIME the doctors and the research men thought that the polio virus entered the human body through the upper membranes of the nose. They swabbed the nostrils of chimpanzees with a powerful astringent and the chimps resisted the terrible contagion.

And so, in one of Canada's great cities, when polio began an epidemic, they did the same with children. But the virus got inside the children without difficulty, killing and crippling the standard number.

Facts concerning polio have been extremely hard to get.

Nevertheless, one thing is definite. Each year the disease is attacking a higher percentage of adults.

You look around your room and wonder at the inappropriateness of the *infantile* in infantile paralysis. A manufacturer of ladies' underwear, a lawyer, yourself, all men in the early thirties. Only a teen-age boy is there to represent youth, and polio brushed him very lightly.

Polio which once confined itself to children, is creating some interesting effects in its experiments with larger human beings.

When the small child is suddenly robbed of his ability to walk, a door slams shut on a very brief experience of active play, and the new world of the cripple is soon all he holds within his memory. The heartbreak is there but without continual reference to the long deep physical habits of unimpaired adult activity.

The brand-new *polio* of thirty-five is overwhelmed with anguish for all he has lost. To this is added the terrifying contemplation of a smashed career, a halted income, the suddenly unbearable responsibility of his home and children. For him the assistance of the National Foundation for Infantile Paralysis is a life raft.

And the wife of this *polio* must suddenly adjust herself to a personal world in which the greatest strength has turned to helplessness.

She has occupied herself with the continuous creation of a home for her husband and her children, and now, quite literally, the walls of it fall down, and she must face the outside world in all directions. Her husband's ordered efforts which brought the necessary money are mysterious to her, and she cannot take his place. He has tumbled out of the familiar world onto a narrow hospital bed. Her children nag tearfully at her to bring him back to them, but she cannot. She is lonely, very frightened, and her only contact with him is along the narrow avenue of *visiting hours*.

In the Hospital for Special Surgery, you are a *polio*

of just this type, and you wait for your wife's arrival with a pressure of eagerness which has come to be by far the strongest feeling you possess.

You must wait until seven o'clock. Your one strong hand lifts again and again to the three-dollar watch which hangs from the crossbar at the head of your bed. As the hour draws near you beg the nurse to hurry with the preparations which must be made. You bathe as best you can, and comb your hair, a fresh pajama top is struggled into. You ask once more if your bed may be rolled up a little way so you may see your visitor with more convenience, but in the interest of your weak back muscles, this is denied. You examine the face of the watch again, and listen for the rush of footsteps in the hall.

At first a distant gathering of voices comes, lighter, fresher, much more energetic than the tiresome drone of nurses and attendants. Then there is the bright *click click* of sharp heels beating towards you. Three wives arrive together, having broken through the barrier at the minute of the hour.

The wife of your friend the pantie manufacturer leads the way into the room, marching purposefully, rather large as his proper mate should be, with beaming face, and both hands clutching a small smoothly wrapped package which you know holds several of his favorite sandwiches. Later you will share in this delicious contraband. Then your friend the lawyer greets his wife, a slender woman who hurries towards him with a graceful stride.

"Hello," your own wife whispers very close.

Her hands catch your face and press it to her own, and you shut your eyes tight, breathing in the soft sweetness of her perfume. She starts to move back so that she can look into your face, but you have been clever, you have been planning this: you reach up with your strong hand and catch the string of the surgical mask which the hospital decrees that she must wear when visiting and snatch it from her face.

This makes her laugh, and her laughter moves all through you.

"I've got to put that thing back on," she says.

"I'll kill you first," you tell her.

Her face is wonderful to see, a small face, full of beauty, white and curving to the darkness of the hair, small nose so handsomely turned, lips lifted with her energetic laughter. The blue eyes glare with affection into yours.

"Kiss me," you say.

"The doctors would die. . . ."

"Fine. Kiss me," you demand. And again the delight of her comes all around you. You catch her with your good hand and press her as close as possible. You feel tears stinging in your eyes. She sobs your name against your ear.

And then she is dancing backward, her eyes staring brightly down.

"You must be getting well," she says.

"Why not?"

She steps back toward the bed. Her hand moves uncertainly to touch her mouth.

"The children . . ."

"Yes?" you say.

"They hate me these days." Her voice comes brighter now. "I mean, positively."

"Why's that?"

"Because I won't bring you home."

"Tell them, I'll be back. Tell them . . ."

And then you stop. For no reason, you simply cannot say the next word, and you see that stricken expression creep across her face. You clear your throat and shift around on your good shoulder.

"Look . . . I've been thinking . . ." you begin.

"Yes, dear."

"About the book. It was almost ready to be taken to the publisher. Just a little more work on it. I'll get up from here and get into a wheel chair soon . . . a few days or so . . . and finish it up."

"Of course you will, it won't be hard for you."

"Nothing to it. In fact, I thought you might . . ."

Again you have difficulty reaching that next word. "Yes?" she says.

"You might phone the editors who have helped me

on it, and tell them that I'll have it ready in a few weeks now."

"That's a wonderful idea. I'll do it tomorrow."

"I'm feeling stronger," you say firmly.

"You're looking so much better."

And then you stop and look into each other's eyes.

"How are your legs?" she asks quietly.

"The doctor found that one muscle . . . I told you. . . ."

"Can you move them now, a little?"

"No," you have to tell her. "No, not yet."

"Don't worry, it will come."

"Of course it will."

You watch each other, and she maneuvers toward the small white metal chair.

She tells you about the children, full of animation now, her voice bouncing around in wonderful imitations of the way you know their voices sound. She is full of news about your friends. You laugh with each other, and you grow warm inside.

But the hour fades away, and a strutting nurse appears to say that visiting is over. You cannot kiss again. The nurse is watching. The surgical mask is back in place and you can see only your wife's anxious eyes.

She catches your hand and holds it tight, and then she is gone toward the doorway. The wives of the lawyer and the pantie manufacturer meet her there and they go out together.

The room is quiet for a moment.

"I got sandwiches," says the pantie manufacturer.

"Swell," says the lawyer.

"That's great," you say.

But the clicking of the sharp, dear heels has faded, and you are listening to the distant chatter of the voices of the wives as they turn in their visitors' passes at the far end of the hall.

VII

The Book

THE BOOK which you have written is not yet a book at all. It is nearly five hundred sheets of typewriting in a brown legal folder, heavily disfigured with pencil markings. But, with the sponsorship of the two well-known editors, a front-rank publishing firm has given you a cash advance against possible future royalties.

The book lies on the high narrow table near the head of your bed, and with your stronger hand you touch it timidly, not wanting to examine its pages. You are not yet physically able to do the added writing which is needed.

You remain smothered by the fact that with you writing must be done sitting upright, with active hands, a typewriter before you—a position and activity now impossible.

Recently, however, strength has been rushing back into your arms and shoulders. Each day, the muscle re-education exercises discover new and stronger movements. You flex your fingers and ponder their efficiency on typewriter keys. At night you struggle to sit up in your bed. All through your body the muscle spasms are lessening, and the pain is fading with it. Your mind is gaining space to think.

Thinking has always been the work you do. You think about problems and events and situations, and then you write messages which seem appropriate.

Now you are thinking about the book's needed reconstruction, and this work provides the first important relief from the paralyzing depression which polio brings with it.

Then, one afternoon very unexpectedly, the two editors who told you from one scrap of writing that your work had value, and encouraged you to write the book, walk into your room. They have caught you between hot packs and the tank, and you are confused.

"This isn't a visiting period . . ." you tell them uncertainly.

"We know that," says the editor, and hands you a bottle of very good sherry. You feel silly, lying flat on your back, holding the bottle in your strong hand.

The editor stares down sharply into your eyes, nose and short beard pointing sharply, too. He is not a smiling man. You have never seen him smile. But the look he gives you now is familiar, reassuring; it is his expression when he talks to you about the writing of a book, prodding, slightly angry.

His wife, co-editor in all his work, does the smiling,

and her dark eyes hold affection and, underneath, a stricken look which is not pity but a kind of anguish, to see you lying there.

"He told them he had to see you on urgent business, and they let us in," she says.

"The book," he says abruptly. "When are you going to finish it?"

"I've been thinking . . ." you tell him.

"Try to shorten it," he says, "and throw out several of the characters. Too many people are saying the same thing."

You nod.

"Will they let you drink the sherry?" he asks.

"Maybe . . . I don't know."

With quick, intent movements, he hails a nurse, talks with her briefly, and in a moment three glasses are brought by an orderly who thoughtfully supplies a corkscrew. The editor opens the bottle and pours the drinks.

"To the book," he says.

You turn sideways in the bed to sip. The wine tastes good.

He prods at you about the writing, his wife making softer comments. He puts down a book for you to read and describes the problems of the man who wrote it. A good deal of time has passed. A nurse is hovering.

"And another thing," he tells you, picking up his hat,

"find time to write something about the way you feel in here, perhaps a few sketches."

You nod once more, and the editors depart.

That night, long after your roommates are asleep, you silently turn on the light above your head. You struggle over on your side and take the legal folder in your stronger hand. You roll to the familiar position on your back, and take out the heavy stack of pages, placing them carefully on your chest. With your thumb and forefinger you count out the twenty-two pages which you know make up the first chapter, and tug these back into the light. Very slowly you start to read.

The people in the book begin to move and talk in the ways you have thought about so deeply. A smooth force catches hold of them. Your mind begins to heat, you have the wondrous feeling of it focusing. The pages turn away, you take up another chapter, and another. The stack of sheets at your right side is growing.

You hear no stirring on the bed of your special friend, the lawyer, but he says:

"What are you up to now?"

"My book. I'm working," you say.

You put down the sheaf of pages and look at him. He stares into your eyes intently.

"I've been watching you for quite a while," he says. "It must be good to work again."

"The book seems all right, the part I've read," you say.

"Writing a book, that must be great." His voice is soft with pride in you.

"I've got some work to do on it," you say.

"You'll get it done, don't worry."

"Once I'm in a wheel chair."

"They say it will take at least another month," he reminds you.

"I can't wait that long."

You watch each other for several minutes.

"I won't bother you," he says, "I'm going back to sleep."

He fights his way over on his side, facing his private stretch of wall, and you go on reading.

Much later you see a familiar white shape beside your bed.

"You've got to turn off your light," the nurse tells you.

For a moment it is difficult for you to swing your attention 'round to her. You have been pulled so deep inside the book, and for some time you have had a pencil in your hand, making notes.

"All right," you say.

The nurse moves closer and helps you rearrange the pages. She puts them back into the folder for you.

"You have been reading more than three hours," she says.

"Did you know . . . ?"

"I saw the light at once, but you were quiet, and looked as if you were working."

"That was nice of you," you say.

"It's hard on a man not to be able to work," she says. She puts the folder carefully back on the table.

"What is this?" she asks.

"A book," you tell her.

"That's wonderful work to do," she says. "I hope it's a big success."

You love her for the kindness which is so much greater than she knows. You are going to say something to her in gratitude, but she reaches up and snaps off the light.

"Now go to sleep," she says, and leaves the room.

You lie thinking further along the course of the story you have written. You dig your way through the cluttered parts near the end, keeping at it until you finish. You know it will be all right, but that you must get into a wheel chair and sit in some quiet corner at a desk.

You struggle hard to sit up now. You get your stronger arm under you, but then you fall back with a thud. Pain knifes up along your spine, and a tiny penetrating headache starts. You try again. Again you fall.

You are panting from your efforts. Again you commence the labored hoisting. The strong arm is firm beneath you, and you are halfway up. You jam in the other arm, and suddenly you reach the center of gravity and lean forward. Pain crawls in the back of your legs.

You sway dizzily, and then bring up your hands for steadiness.

You know you've got to practice this. You begin to lower yourself, and, balance lost, your weight brings you thudding down. You rest for a moment, and then climb up again. This time it is easier.

"Nothing's going to stop you now," you whisper to yourself.

The next afternoon the doctor commends you on your new-found ability to sit upright.

"You can have that wheel chair an hour a day," he says.

He turns to leave your bed. You try to catch his arm and nearly tumble sideways.

"Yes?" he asks.

"I wonder . . . is there some place where I could be alone to work?"

"Some place alone?" questions the charge-nurse sharply. "Now that's ridiculous. . . ."

The doctor stares thoughtfully at you for a moment, and then turns to her.

"Let him use the tank-room for an hour after three o'clock," he says.

"But doctor," she says, "hospital regulations make it necessary . . ."

But now he is definitely advancing to the next bed, and she makes a double-handed gesture of defeat.

You let yourself down very carefully to your usual flat position in the bed. An hour a day, alone in a place to work. You turn towards the wall and think again about your book.

VIII

Will I Walk Again . . . ?

ONE DAY a development of staggering importance oc-
curs.

You clench the muscle of your right leg above the
knee as you have done so many times, since the doctor
first discovered that it was alive, and this time the knee
lifts a fraction of an inch. You think your eyes have de-
ceived you, and you strain once more. Your whole leg
lifts very slightly from the bed.

You call out to your friend, the lawyer:

"Watch this . . . it's something new!"

Again you perform the tiny hitch upward with your
knee.

"Holy heaven," murmurs your friend in the prayerful
tones with which miracles are observed.

You twitch the knee, turning it slightly this way and
that. The pressure of triumph is so great that you find it
difficult to breath.

"Hey, get up and look at this!" your friend calls down
to the pantie manufacturer.

"I can't even lift my nose, you miserable character,"

says this friend farther down the room. His voice is terribly eager, though, and he waves his hand at you. "Tell me about it," he demands.

"He can lift his leg, really lift it!" shouts the lawyer.

"And here's another thing," you say, and turn the knee slightly back and forth.

"Now he's throwing that leg all over the bed!" comes the lawyer's acclamation.

"That's wonderful, really wonderful," says the pantie manufacturer, and the pure feeling in his tone causes an unexpected pain to twist in you. You know the terrible extent of his own paralysis.

"I'm telling you I *know* the guy is going to walk!" the lawyer states.

The pain turns towards a deeper point within you. Your own hands and arms are nearly normal now, while one side of the lawyer's upper body remains useless.

"I don't know," you falter, "it may not mean a thing."

"Don't talk that way," the lawyer says.

"Don't be a meathead, buddy," says the pantie manufacturer. "This means that you'll strut out of here like my old army sergeant."

You stare down at the miraculous leg.

"I'll have to ask the doctor," you say.

An attendant walks in with full water pitchers, and at once the lawyer challenges him, "What about this . . . he can move his leg! Move it!"

"That's fine," says the attendant, the indifference in

his voice barely hidden. "All of you men will recover, it's just a matter of time." His stride is undisturbed, and he only glances at your legs as he passes, not bothering to ask which one.

Your friends continue to discuss your accomplishment in tones that ring with joy for you.

"It may not be important," you say quietly, but you are shouted down.

You want to be off by yourself to think about your leg. It does not seem fair to concentrate upon it in the presence of your less fortunate friends.

Your work periods in the tank-room have been extended and you have learned to sit more comfortably in your wheel chair. But this one day the fascination of the book you are finishing does not hold you. You sit quietly, examining your leg. You cannot move it in your present sitting position, but this does not matter. You can remember its performance.

Suddenly you feel sure that you will walk again, that this is only the beginning of the most remarkable recovery in the history of polio. A strange sense of strength surges through your body.

It is quite a thing to walk, you decide. To suddenly thrash your legs into a run because you are almost too late to catch the train, and then to lift your leg to the high step and ram your body upward with its strength. You take your hands and move your knees together, out again. They waggle with weakness, but you have seen your right leg twist and lift on the white blanket of the bed, and hope is making you breathless again.

You can remain no longer in your narrow workroom. you wheel out into the hall, and take the elevator to the hospital's solarium. You notice with satisfaction the efficient legs of doctors, nurses and the scattered visitors of private patients. You catch the eye of a few of these brisk people and smile at them companionably. If they should ask you how you are feeling, you would enjoy describing the remarkable strength of your right leg.

Crowding as close as you can to one of the solarium's wide windows, you stare down six stories into the busy intersection of Forty-second Street and Second Avenue. People are walking in all directions. You examine them carefully. They are so bold. They step out with carefree swiftness against the traffic light. They bound up to the curbs. They make you laugh with the quickness and dexterity of all their movements.

Your thoughts turn to the doctor, and excitement leaps up in you. What will he say? What *can* he say when he watches that lift and that twitching back and forth?

The hours roll away. In your bed you prepare yourself carefully for the doctor's visit. You tie a narrow binder around your middle. In a sitting position you twitch the knee several times, and lift the leg just once.

You must not tire the muscles before the doctor's inspection.

Your friends are full of admonitions.

"Take your time," the lawyer says.

"Don't just lift your leg, turn it the way you can," you are instructed by the pantie manufacturer.

The doctor comes into the room, followed by his retinue of therapists, nurses and other doctors who listen intently to his every word. It is his habit to begin his rounds in the far end of the room.

But, your friend the lawyer cannot contain himself.

"Doctor, he can lift his leg," he calls out.

The doctor turns to peer at him, then follows his excited directions to your bed.

"Your leg?" says the doctor, his eyes smiling with their cool blue light. "What is this you have to show me?"

You whip back the light covering. You twitch your knee this way and that. You clench the narrow area of muscle with all your might, and with a jerk your leg lifts higher than ever before.

The doctor straightens from his examination and turns to your friends who strain forward attentively in their beds.

"You all know about this, I am sure," he says.

A chorus of assent answers him. The other doctors and the company laugh loudly at this. For them it is quite an amusing interlude. But your doctor's lips scarcely lift, and when he turns back to you, there are shadows in his eyes.

"What do you want me to tell you?" he asks quietly.

You can feel that the attention of your friends is crowding toward your bed.

"Will I walk again?" you ask.

The doctor touches your shoulder gently with his fingers, as he did on his first visit to your bed. His eyes are fixed on the window.

"I can't tell you that," he says, and the shadow is in his voice now, and you know it is a peculiar kind of sadness. "This is a strange disease. I *think* this leg of yours will lift higher and higher, and grow strong. But I don't know. Not yet."

The fingers on your shoulder grip in gently, then he turns away. He pauses only briefly by the other beds, and then the room slips back to quiet behind the clatter of his following.

"He didn't know . . ." the lawyer says.

You watch your leg. You lift it and twitch it this way and that.

IX

Birthday Party

DAY AFTER DAY you think about your children.

Now that the first pain and depression of polio have passed, the borders of your new world have extended beyond the edges of your bed, but they are still much narrower than before the disease hit you. They encompass only a score of people, the least important of these being your dearest friends, and at the center of the group, burning in your heart every waking hour, are your wife and children. You no longer have time for anyone else, and, as it now seems certain that your recovery will be slow and difficult, your instincts tell you that the world beyond these few people no longer can be trusted.

Your wife is with you every visiting period, always bursting eagerly through the doorway on the minute of the hour, her dauntless smile lifting you like strong hands. And at such times friends pour in upon you in whatever quantity your wife decrees.

But children are not allowed, and daily your anxiety grows concerning what they will think of you now that you can no longer walk. With your wife, you already have faced the differences there might be in your life, but a boy of three years and a girl of six have no ability to cast their understanding into the future. They live with complete intensity in each moment as it comes. You fear they will examine you and find you very different.

Such feelings are aggravated by the fact that your birthday is upon you, and you want desperately to have them with you then, if only for a little while. Your wife and you have discussed ways and means of doing this, and checked the matter with the administration office of the hospital. You asked the permission of the physician in charge, who took the request under advisement.

Suddenly one afternoon all sources of authority concur. Your wife may bring the children to the hospital promptly at seven in the evening, to be escorted to the lecture hall where you will be waiting in your wheel chair.

At once you become panicky, and think of having your wife call the whole thing off. You do not sleep that night, and it seems that the old, almost forgotten aching has returned to your legs.

In the morning the charge-nurse asks you if you are feeling badly, and you assure her that you were never better. Your roommates are understanding. The lawyer, who is still very shaky emotionally, cries when you discuss the whole affair carefully with him. The pantie manufacturer declares again and again how much he envies you. Even the teen-age boy speaks wisely of how successful the party is sure to be.

You remain very nervous throughout the day. Over and over again you practice the slight movements which have returned to your right leg. You try to decide whether or not you should demonstrate these accomplishments to your children. A decision on this terribly important matter is too much for you and finally you turn to the pantie manufacturer, who is very intelligent about nearly everything.

"My advice," he says, making a solemn downbeat with his cigarette, "is no."

He offers you a cigarette and lights it for you with fatherly care.

"The way I look at this," he continued, "as long as they see you sitting quiet in the chair, they'll just figure that you're sitting down because you want to. You used to sit down quite a bit at home, didn't you?"

"Yes," you tell him.

He gives his marvelously expressive shrug.

"Okay, then," he confirms.

You know that he has advised you well, and you are very grateful.

By the middle of the afternoon, you are deep in worry concerning what you should wear. You hate the idea of your convict-looking hospital robe. You fret about whether you should allow your feet to be seen or keep them covered.

You realize with the slow sinking of despair that you really have no clothes to wear. Before being sent to this hospital, direct from diagnosis, all clothing was taken from you, and you were wrapped naked in a blanket, like the plague victims of several centuries ago. You have only the unpressed bed-shirts and loin-binders of this place of isolation.

And then, two marvelous events take place.

First, you receive as a birthday gift from one of those precious twenty people a handsome sports jacket of softest corduroy. You put it on at once, and miraculously, it fits. You are elated at your good fortune until you realize that you have no shirt to wear with it. There seems no way that you can get hold of a white shirt without giving away the surprise to your wife.

But the pantie manufacturer, though he is still riveted by paralysis to his bed, is not a man to be dismayed by such problems. An hour later there is a fine white shirt at your bedside, exactly your size. He has simply bribed an attendant to sneak out and buy you one.

"You got to have a shirt, you miserable character," he explains, making another gesture with his cigarette.

At fifteen minutes before seven you wheel yourself from bed to bed, dressed in your new finery, your legs neatly wrapped in a white blanket. Each pair of eyes is very warm, sharing your triumph. The lawyer tells a joke about it, but there are tears in his eyes again.

At five minutes to seven, you are sitting alone in the

lecture hall. The clock in the wall is very slow. Then there is a rush of excited noises in the hall, and the door bursts open.

They crowd through together, and then your little boy comes towards you like a rocket. His voice goes yelping like a puppy's. He dives into your blanket-swathed knees, clutching them in his arms, his small hands digging painfully into the muscles along the backs of your legs. You try to reach down to him, but the unsteady muscles in your back give way and you lurch awkwardly, barely saving yourself from a crash to the floor.

Startled, your boy steps backward slowly. Your wife rushes to you to hold your shoulders, then turns toward him.

"You must be careful of Daddy's legs . . . !" she says.

"Oh no," you manage, "it's all right."

But your little boy continues to back slowly away.

You feel a light pressure on your hand where it tightly grips the hand-rim of one of the chair's big wheels. You jerk your head in that direction, and find your daughter, nearly six, staring deep into your eyes. There is a tightened expression on her smooth little face.

"You *can* walk, can't you, Daddy . . . you really *can?*" she asks in a small voice low and shaking with intensity.

"Well, I . . ." you begin.

"You mustn't say that, dear," your wife whispers to her. "I told you . . ."

You catch your wife's arm, and everything in the big room is very quiet.

Quickly then, your wife sets in motion the ritual of the birthday party. There are presents for you and a cake. You ask your children a running line of questions, and soon they are shouting down each other in descriptions of their important plans and doings.

They dash around the room investigating its points of interest, and with your wife, you watch them.

The hands of the big wall clock have turned with dismaying swiftness to eight o'clock. Your wife calls the children to your wheel chair, and they repeat rather forced exclamations about your birthday. Your little boy touches the hand-rim and tries to move the wheel a little. He is watchful.

Suddenly your little girl bursts out, "Please walk, Daddy . . . please . . . !" And then her smooth face is distorted with sobbing.

Your wife hurries them away with almost hysterical good-bys, and you find your fingers are gripping desperately hard upon the hand-rims of your motionless wheel chair.

X

Job of Work

A FRIEND stands beside your bed. Stocky, with a heavy head and somber dark eyes. He has always been an impatient man, and now you watch him fumble frantically with the white surgical mask which all of your visitors are supposed to wear, and then thrust the stub of his cigar under it. He clasps his hands behind his back, tugs up his head and teeters on his toes.

He is very impatient about your having polio.

"Well, what about your legs?" he barks, with an eyebrow grimace that is almost savage.

You feel very steady, watching him from your sitting position on the bed. You cannot help smiling. It is a good thing to be absolutely certain of another man's friendship.

"My legs are still a mystery," you tell him.

"Mystery?" he does not like this explanation. He is a thirty-nine-year-old corporation lawyer whose drive and brilliance have already carried him to an annual income of a quarter of a million dollars. Large companies pay him handsomely for reducing the mysteries of taxation and pension-planning to workable simplic-ity. The word *mystery* is an annoyance.

"My right leg has begun to move," you tell him with a patient smile.

"We can count on complete recovery for that one, I suppose?"

You caution him with a gesture.

"Nobody knows," you tell him. "I hope to use it with-out a brace."

"Don't be childish," he says. "Of course you will."

He pokes down at your weaker leg which is nearest him.

"What about this one?" he demands.

You shrug.

"You can't just *lie* here!" he explodes.

"That's what you think," you say.

"Listen, I need you to do a job of work for me. It's a tough job, important for a lot of reasons."

You stare at him with some surprise. He is not treat-ing you like a patient in a hospital. And you realize that he is frightening you.

You worked with him on a number of projects when you were *well*. But now he ought to take more notice of your condition.

He eyes you moodily. The surgical mask has gone askew on his face, and the unlighted cigar stub is clamped back into place.

"You need money, don't you?" he asks.

"Of course I do." You are irritated with the relentlessness of his attack.

"All right, he says. "I've got to chairman a tax study session of top businessmen at the Waldorf. I've got only three days to prepare for it. I brought my material." He stoops and grabs up his battered briefcase. His impatient fingers rip down the zipper, and he clutches out a stack of papers. "I've laid it out in lawyer talk," he tells you. "I want you to rewrite the whole thing for me. One piece should be sort of a mimeographed folder for the members, another should be a press release . . . organize my own remarks . . . you know." He dumps the papers between your legs. "All right?"

"What the devil are you trying to do . . . !" you say. His face is bland.

"Get some work out of you, you lazy lout," he explains.

Perhaps out of habit, you pick up the papers.

"The way I've been feeling, I don't see how . . ." you begin.

"You'll have to work fast," your friend tells you. "And bill me for the job as soon as you get it done."

"Look here, I didn't say . . . !"

He bends down, pushing the papers towards the wall, placing them more firmly in your possession. Again he pokes down at your weaker leg.

"Do something about this one, you hear me? Why have only one leg when two are better?"

You have to laugh at him, this wildly impatient friend of yours. He looks up and his eyes grin. When your laughter quiets down, you find that you're not nearly so frightened about the job.

"Only three days?" you say.

"That's plenty of time," he says. "I've seen you do jobs like this overnight."

"Okay," you tell him.

"I've got to run along now," he says at once. He snatches up his briefcase and jams the zipper back into place. He sets the surgical mask partially into place.

"You're really quite a character," you tell him.

Though his mouth is hidden, his eyes tell you that he is smiling.

"The next time I come back here, I want to see you walking," he says.

"I'll try," you say.

He waves, and moves with his quick heavy stride out of the room.

You pick up the papers and glance through the first section swiftly. You are a little surprised to find that already your mind is working with the material, cutting it down, simplifying, highlighting the important points. You roll over to your side and take a pencil from the drawer of your table. You get deeper into the job of work, making notes. You begin to think about your typewriter and the words you will use in your several translations of the involved material. You feel yourself begin to heat up inside, the way you always do when you are working.

You are now allowed to sit in the wheel chair for three hours at a stretch. You take the job with you into the tank-room. You have fastened a wide board to the arms of your wheel chair. This is your desk, and your typewriter is already on it. You separate the papers on the leather-covered treating-table at your right side. You feel yourself functioning totally.

It makes you chuckle to know how little you need your legs for the work you do best. Perhaps you will never *play* efficiently again, but, by God, you will work as well as ever.

Your notes are already filling out to paragraphs. You are sweating very nicely. You've got your mind around the job of work.

Several days later you have a surprise for your wife when she arrives for a visiting period. It is an open envelope with your friend's business address typed on it.

"Oh, you're writing him a letter?" she says.

"It's quite a letter," you tell her. "Better take a look at it."

She takes out the folded sheet and smooths it open Her eyes grow round with surprise.

"You're sending him a bill?"

You nod.

"For what?"

"I did a job of work for him," you say.

"This is quite a lot of money . . ."

"I did quite a job."

She folds up the sheet and puts it back in the envelope.

"You're not waiting for your legs . . ." she says.

"I haven't that much time," you tell her.

"I've always been proud of you," she says quietly. "Did I ever tell you that?"

"Oh, maybe. Once or twice."

She takes your hand and grips it hard, the way a man does in a handshake.

"We're going to be all right," she says.

And you feel that you have won a prize beyond all value.

XI

Wheel Chairs Roll in All Directions

YOU ARE GROWING STRONGER.

Every morning you exercise the muscles of your stomach and back. Lying flat, you grab your legs as far down as you can reach and lift your body up and forward. Already you need the hold for little more than balancing. Your right leg is lifting higher from the bed and is responding more vigorously to its muscle re-education.

As a reward for this advancement, you are allowed more time in your wheel chair.

Not all of this time do you use in work. There are two other rooms in the ward, and you visit from bed to bed. A former New York City police officer smiles up at you grimly from a helpless position on his back. A boy of sixteen, already nearly fully recovered, chatters in the strange, quick, witty vernacular of his generation. An established dentist of thirty talks with you interestingly of the world events reported in that morning's papers, his paralyzed right arm, the arm upon which the practice of his profession depends, locked tight in an airplane splint.

Your wheel chair takes you everywhere.

There is one man with whom you do not make friends along these journeys. This dismays you, until the others in the room tell you that no one can get next to him. That he is a dope, a surly misfit.

"We call him Droopy," they tell you quietly behind their hands.

Droopy has a wide-boned strong-looking face, but the disease which robbed him of his strength has transformed it to a gaunt mask where expressions catch and hold stiffly. His eyes stare sullenly, one of them cocked slightly out, the heavy eyelids drooping. He growls in his bed all day, cursing at himself because his legs will not move as he wrenches his body into new positions.

For hours at a time he lies with his face to the wall and will not heed the questions of his roommates. He does not speak to them. His hair has not been cut since he reached the hospital, and now the shaggy mane twists around his eyes.

"Look, Droopy," one of his roommates says to him one day, "if you can't afford a haircut, I'll pay for it. You look like an animal."

"Go to hell," says Droopy.

When a man does not communicate with those around him he creates ill will, and without deviation Droopy adds to this store. He shuts out those who would have been his friends. He snarls at the nurse, and is reported. After he learns to sit up in bed, he turns towards the windows and stares into space for long periods. Once a sleepless roommate hears him sob all night.

"Droopy acted like he'd gone off his rocker," he relates. "He beat the wall with his fists, he groaned like he was being strangled."

It is agreed by all that Droopy needs psychiatry as well as hotpacks. The only important fact in your possession concerning him is that he is twenty-two years old.

One day a pleasant woman arrives from the National Foundation for Infantile Paralysis. She goes straight to Droopy's bed.

She identifies herself, and at once Droopy says in a voice oddly soft for him:

"How is my wife?"

From the conversation which follows Droopy's story is noted by the other patients in his room.

"Your wife is going to live," the woman says.

"But the baby?" Droopy asks.

"We told you," says the woman quietly, and hesitating as long as she can. "The baby died."

"That's right," says Droopy. "I was thinking about it the other night, and that's the way I remembered it."

He stares at her sullenly.

"You're sure about it?" he asks.

"Yes," the woman says.

"I still get mixed up about it," Droopy says. "Everything was all right when I got polio, and then right afterwards, my wife . . ."

"It was the shock," says the woman from the Foundation quickly, "but she is all right now."

"I was pretty sick for a while, and everything got mixed up," says Droopy.

"You were very sick. You had a good deal of delirium."

"If I could see my wife, I think I would be all right," says Droopy.

"She's still not able to visit you, I'm afraid," the woman says.

"It all happened so quick," says Droopy. "I had a new job, I was saving money, and all of a sudden, I couldn't move my legs."

"We'll see that you get a good start again," the woman tells him. "That's our job at the Foundation."

"I didn't have any folks," says Droopy. "My wife is about all I've ever had."

"We understand," the woman says.

"I want to see my wife as soon as possible," says Droopy.

The woman assures him that everything will be taken care of in the best way.

"I haven't had much education," says Droopy, "I've got to work at ordinary jobs. Without my legs, I'm scared. Maybe I can't take care of my wife. I think about that all the time."

"The Foundation will help you all along the way," the woman tells him.

"I want to thank you people," says Droopy, and his roommates are astounded at the gentleness of his voice, and the broken way he tries to smile. "Without you, I'd have gone nuts lying in this bed, not able to help my wife."

The woman from the Foundation touches his arm and Droopy does not turn away.

"Things will work out," she says.

"We'll see," says Droopy.

Your wheel chair takes you in all directions through the ward. You have friends in every corner of every room. You find interesting items in the papers concerning the Police Department, and the police officer relates anecdotes which bear upon them. The teenagers gather and are polite enough to take you into their peculiar, wayward conversations. The dentist is opposed to the Government's stand on China, and his vehemence causes his airplane splint to jerk quickly back and forth.

But Droopy lies facing the wall, or stares sullenly out of the window. He now says hello when you pass by, but his thoughts do not reach in your direction. Occasionally you hear him curse his lifeless legs.

XII

No Child Is a Cripple!

THE GYMNASIUM has windows on three sides, and it is packed, in an orderly way, with the equipment of muscle rehabilitation.

You sit in your wheel chair near the entrance, waiting your turn to exercise on one of the mats. You have not yet made the tremendous transition from wheel chair to upright standing. You are strengthening the muscles of your arms and back and stomach for the ordeal which this will be.

There are several children in the big room.

You watch a little boy of not more than five or six work his way forward to the edge of his small wheel chair. His legs are thrust out rigidly by two long leg-braces. You see the glint of the metal which locks in against the heels of his scuffed brown shoes. He grasps the two rails which lead the way into the parallel bars and tries to haul himself to his feet.

But something goes wrong. He has not been properly fastened together.

The chief gym therapist—a young woman in her middle twenties, very pretty, a slender, lovely figure, dark hair and smooth white skin—rushes over to him. He is sagging badly, holding onto one rail desperately, but making no sound. The therapist knows just what to do. She yanks up his tiny shirt, and you see the tube of leather and steel which holds his small body firm. One series of loops and cleats in this harness have not been closed.

"Just a minute, Ralph," she tells him in a soft, reassuring voice. "I'll fix the darned old thing."

Ralph smiles up at her, his solemn little face suddenly aglow with friendliness.

The harness properly adjusted, she slides his shirt back and smooths it down. He struggles upright on his rigid legs without her help.

"That's the boy," she tells him. "Now go to work. Show me what you can do."

His face knots with concentration below the shock of dark hair. He lunges forward and catches one of the adjustable parallel bars which have been set very low. With a terrific spasm of his little body, he drags his left foot forward several inches. Then he catches the other bar with his other hand. Again effort galvanizes his body, and the feet drag forward together.

You wheel down the room toward him, stopping several feet away.

"Is he a *polio?*" you ask the therapist.

"Yes," she says, "a bad one. It hit him nearly everywhere."

"Will his legs come back?" you ask.

She shakes her head, her rich dark hair moving this way and that. "There's nothing in them," she says. "He has been this way for nearly two years now."

The little boy has struggled to a standing position between the parallel bars, and remains there resting. His tiny shoulders heave with his breathing. The therapist waits a moment and then says, "All right, Ralph, go on."

The boy's back is toward you. He half turns his head and smiles. Then he hunches forward, thrusts his hands out along the bars, grips, and, with enormous effort, drags his feet after him a few inches. He keeps this up in a rocking motion that is almost frenzied.

He reaches the end of the bars and turns around. He watches the face of the therapist with solemn eyes.

"That was wonderful," she tells him, and his smile bursts towards her in a shower of light.

The therapist goes on about her business. Somewhere behind you, a little girl has begun to cry. You sit there, watching the boy. He catches your eye and grins. You wave to him. Then he ducks his head, and begins his awful struggle back along the bars. At the end of them, he stands resting. He is near you now.

"That's quite a trick, the way you get along in there," you tell him.

He stares at you eagerly. "Are you a *polio?*" he asks. You tell him that you are.

"I can walk, can't I?" he asks, and his eagerness has grown to something terribly intense.

"I guess you can," you tell him. "I guess that's a fact, Ralph."

He is very pleased. He smiles and tugs his stiffly corseted body back and forth.

"You can walk, too," he says.

"I'm not so sure about that," you say.

For a moment his little face is stricken, and his eyes grow round and dark with anxiety.

"Oh yes . . . !" he says, almost shouting. "Oh yes, you can too walk!"

"I'm going to try to learn," you tell him.

"Everybody can walk," he says, jerking his head sideways and tightening his mouth. "I don't walk very well yet, because I'm too little."

"How old are you, Ralph?" you ask.

"I'm only three years old," he says.

You are surprised that he should be so young, but he nods his head emphatically, and you do not question him further.

The therapist steps back beside you.

"Turn around, Ralph, and go back the other way. You're doing awfully well this morning."

The radiance of his smile rushes at her. He twists around between the bars, and soon is hunching and grabbing his way along, dragging his feet after him inches at a time.

"Only three years old . . . ?" you ask the therapist in a whisper.

Her face is sad as she looks down.

"I heard him tell you that, but I'm afraid it's not the truth. Ralph has passed his sixth birthday."

"But why . . . ?"

The therapist makes a helpless gesture with her hand.

"He knows that babies can't walk, and that some very small children have a hard time trying. So he insists that he is never more than three. Sometimes he says that he is only two and a half."

Behind you somewhere another child begins to whimper, and the therapist moves away.

Ralph turns with heavy clumping at the far end of the parallel bars. He sees that you are still there, and an expression of intense pleasure touches his face. He hurries towards you as best he can. He has something important to say.

He stops as close as he can get to you. He is gasping from his exertions, and his rigid little body sways upon his tired arms. But his smile is like a shaft of brilliant sunlight in the room.

"We can walk!" he tells you.

"Sure we can . . . everybody can . . . !" you reply with emphasis.

This makes him laugh. His little voice goes crowing up in triumph.

XIII

Christmas Visit

THERE IS A TALL APARTMENT BUILDING reaching upward on a slant quite a distance beyond your hospital window. You like New York's blue light of evening, and quite often at this time, you survey the terraces of the building's penthouse floor, and, above this, the line of silly gargoyles which some overelaborate architect had placed there.

On this evening, a marvelous change has been wrought in the vista. A Christmas tree, bejeweled with colored lights, tops the terrace wall.

You call out to your friend the lawyer, pointing.

"You say that Christmas isn't going to come this year. . . . Look at that," you tell him.

"It'll come, but not for us, that's what I mean," he says.

Nevertheless he follows the direction of your hand.

"It's pretty," he says after a moment.

You both look at the tree for a while. The blue evening atmosphere which is New York's special possession is changing, darkening to purple. The lights of the tree are growing brighter.

"We always decorated our tree on Christmas Eve," you tell your friend.

He nods at you, smiling. "And then surprised the kids with it on Christmas morning."

"We'd tell them Santa Claus decorated the tree, besides filling the stocking."

"That's a good idea," your friend approves.

"But this year, I don't see how it can be done that way. My wife needs me to help. We always have a big tree, from floor to ceiling. I always trim the top, standing on a ladder."

"When you had legs," says your friend.

"Naturally," you say.

You lie for quite a long time looking at the lighted tree perched so beautifully on its narrow stone cliff. The night gets black around it, and it becomes magnificent.

"I'd like to go home for Christmas," says your friend quietly.

Your friend the pantie manufacturer is observing your conversation intently.

"That would be very, very nice," he now says in a soft voice.

"Legs or no legs?" you ask.

"Legs or no legs!" shouts the lawyer, and the pantie manufacturer makes an emphatic gesture.

"I don't suppose there's any possibility of it," you say.

"No," says the lawyer. "This is a hospital, and we've got polio."

But the following day an announcement is made.

Actually, it is another message from the National Foundation for Infantile Paralysis, that surprising organization which now guides your lives. The Foundation is making arrangements for all of you to spend the Christmas week end with your families, whether you walk, sit in a wheel chair, or must remain on a stretcher.

Some day, you decide, the full story of the Foundation's work will be told so truly and so clearly that knowledge of it will join the traditions of the country, which are passed on in simple language from one generation to the next.

In the hospital, excitement at the Christmas news surges through the ward.

Men talk with happy violence and in detail about their wives and children, the layout of their homes, the way the front walk slopes, the size of the rooms of their apartments. They discuss with tense faces the problems which they will face in moving from their beds at home to vital points inside their bathrooms. They measure with hands apart in mid-air the height of their favorite easy chairs.

"Men," says the pantie manufacturer, shooting a keen glance around the half circle of patients who have crowded their wheel chairs into our room, "if you can't navigate around your place any other way, crawl!"

They yell with laughter at this. They stare into each other's eyes, and make crazy, happy gestures with their fists.

That night, in the darkness, your friend the lawyer speaks quietly of the other side of all your feelings.

"I'm scared," he says. "My wife . . . the kids . . . they haven't seen me try to move. . . ."

In each bed, there is a wondering and fearfully urgent kind of planning. You go over all spaces in your homes painstakingly, measuring, scheming. Your throat goes dry again and again, and you stare up at the black ceiling, praying that you will not make the people at home pity you too much.

The brothers of the pantie manufacturer are careful and very strong. You are carried in your wheel chair from their station-wagon into the lobby of the building where you have your apartment. Your wife and the biggest of the brothers go with you into the elevator.

"The children are hiding," your wife says swiftly. "As soon as you get in the apartment you must say, 'Where are they? I must be in the wrong place!'"

You are at your door. Your wife opens it, and your friend's brother pushes your chair inside and quickly says good-by. He doesn't give you time to thank him.

The dear, familiar look of your home catches you like a fist clenching inside your chest.

"Say it . . ." whispers your wife.

"Where are they?" you manage. "I don't understand it . . . this must be the wrong . . ."

In his close-by hiding-place your little boy yells with delight, and then they both come dancing into view.

"I'm a cowboy!" cries the boy with wild distraction, shooting his toy pistol from a crouched position at nothing at all.

"Our Christmas tree . . ." sings your daughter. "It's the biggest one we ever had!"

They rush into your arms.

Later, with the children in bed, you lie on the couch and watch your wife finish the tree's decorations. It is not so loaded with ornaments as formerly, in fact around the top it is rather bare, yet when at last the lights are turned on, it floods the room with the greatest beauty you have ever seen.

There are struggles from the couch to the wheel chair, from the chair into your bed, but the night grows quiet and you are safe. You remember the unbearably excited dreams of Christmas Eve when you were a child; and you think of the gifts and loaded stockings in your own front room where the living Christmas tree stands watch. Your household is deeply asleep, and you are watching with the tree.

The next morning is only in its faint beginning when
the children scramble from their bedroom into yours.
The boy calls for everyone to follow him, and is at the
door, when the girl orders him to wait for you. They
stare at you sitting on the edge of the bed.

They must watch you struggle now. The room is quiet
and you joke about your silly legs. Advancing with your
chair you throw open the door. Your wife dashes
through to turn on the tree lights, and the children move
with soft, almost tiptoe steps into the miracle of Christmas morning.

You are in your big chair now, your legs thrown out
at ease. Your wife moves busily about, clearing away
the fabulous debris of the Christmas dinner. Your little
girl suddenly comes close, clasps her arms around
your neck and whispers fiercely, "Stand up, Daddy!"

Your wife stops near you.

"What did she say?" she asks.

"She wants me to stand."

"You mustn't say that to Daddy, not yet, dear," your
wife tells her.

She stares down sideways at the floor, her smooth
face growing tense.

"The next time I come home . . ." you tell her
stoutly, "you'll see . . . I'll get up like a jumping jack."

Your boy laughs at this, and the girl smiles wanly

once, before making a hopping advance toward her newest doll.

You turn towards the Christmas tree. The lights are dim now, with so much sunlight in the room.

XIV

Walking Is Only a Trick

THE SMALLEST POLIO PATIENT in the hospital is a little girl, barely two years old.

A tiny harness of soft white duck is strapped around her body, with two short, wide reins of the same material attaching at the shoulders. Her chubby left leg is held firm and straight by a full brace of leather and light metal, which they tell you is a miniature replica of the one which you probably will wear upon your same leg.

The little arms are lifted in the balancing gesture of all babies. The chief therapist holds the reins tightly in her hands as she crouches over the curly head. The child steps high with her undamaged leg and hauls the braced leg after it.

The grown men watching along the corridor raise a cheer.

The child laughs at them and claps her hands.

"Walking is only a trick," the chief therapist reminds them all.

Always when the doctor makes his rounds on Thursday, you are ready for him, sitting in your wheel chair.

This is the special day in your relations with him—the day he makes decisions concerning changes in the course of your treatments. You are always nervous, highly expectant. In all your life you have never felt such reliance on another man, or such confidence in his judgment. It is his habit never to tell you anything directly, unless in answer to a question. He simply lays his hands on your legs in several places and asks you to try to perform certain movements. Shortly after his departure, the charge-nurse tells you of his current decision.

The doctor makes his brisk advance into the room. He makes the circle of the beds, taking more time with each patient than on other days. He stops before your chair and looks down into your eyes with his level blue stare.

"Stand him on his feet," he tells two of the male therapists standing near by.

Fear shoots through you. The therapists move toward your arms.

"I'm not sure . . ." you begin.

"You're not sure about what?" asks the doctor.

"I've never been even halfway up . . . I don't think I can actually stand . . ."

"Of course you can," the doctor tells you. He motions to the therapists.

They take you above each elbow.

"Put your arms around their necks," directs the doctor.

The struggle upward seems to take a long time. Your legs are under you, feeling like two strands of cooked spaghetti. The doctor stoops and deftly pushes back your knees so that they can lock under your weight.

"Hold them there," he orders.

You clench the muscles above your knees, as you have been taught. You are sweating with fright.

"Put your hands on their necks and balance yourself," the doctor says. You do this and then he tells them to take their hands away from your body. You are standing.

You look down at the floor, an immense distance, and see your shoes placed just as they used to be before polio took the life from your legs. You cannot see your legs, you are afraid to lean that far forward.

"Very good," the doctor says.

You try to lift your head to look at him. You have to jerk it, using great effort. You see with surprise that you are much taller than he. His white eyebrows are lifted quizzically as he peers at you.

"You see," he says, "there's nothing to it."

"I . . . feel . . . fifty feet high . . . !" you tell him.

He smiles. "We've probably stretched you up an inch or two, but not that much," he says.

You are almost sobbing with the triumph you feel inside.

"Now lift your right leg," he tells you. "Step out as if you were going to climb right through that doorway."

"I couldn't . . ."

"Yes you can," he says.

The chief therapist, a young woman of driving, intelligent personality whom you have come to respect, touches his arm. "Doctor, that leg is very weak. He won't be able to lift it, and if he tries . . ."

"Nonsense," he tells her gently. "I've been watching the leg. It will lift."

He peers up at you with that quizzical expression.

You think terribly hard about your leg. In your mind, you say with all your might: *Lift* . . . throw out the foot . . . !

You feel it coming. Suddenly your leg is swinging clear. You tell your foot to push its way out. You glance down and see the foot appear in the air and then come down with a little flop. You have taken a step.

Now you know that the tears are running down your cheeks. You see the doctor indistinctly, and it seems to you that he is grinning, an expression you have never seen before. The chief therapist congratulates you wholeheartedly.

"Now you can sit down," says the doctor.

You lurch backward and the two therapists lower

you to the chair. You feel very tired and sit with your head bent down, while your friends in their beds shout out their approval of what you have done.

"When will I get my brace?" you ask the doctor.

"In a few days now," he tells you.

"What will happen then?" you want to know.

"We'll teach you how to walk," he says.

The hospital's smallest *polio,* with all the balance and dexterity of a two-year-old with one tiny leg locked in leather and dura-aluminum, tries to turn at the far end of the corridor. She falls, hands grasping at the air, and only the quick pull of the chief therapist on the reins of her white harness saves her from a thumping on the floor.

Fright makes the child cry, and the grown men watching from their wheel chairs turn their eyes away.

But soon they hear the chortle and the sharp, glad directions with which the little patient commonly accompanies her exercises. They see the little girl come stepping, dragging, stepping, dragging towards them once again.

"You show them now," says the therapist with the gallant urging children love. "Walking's a trick anyone can learn!"

XV

Departure

THE LONG BRACE clicks and locks smartly at the knee, and leaning against the wall, you stand erect.

Today the floor is only twenty feet away instead of fifty, as it was upon your first ascent to the normal human walking position. The rods of the brace gleam in slender perfection downward, your thin naked leg between them.

"I still wish you had made this thing out of aluminum," you say to Lou, one of the world's great brace-makers, who stands near by.

"Quit your beefing," says Lou. "You were six foot two when they brought you in, and you've probably been stretched another couple of inches. It takes steel to hold a man your size."

"I don't mean to imply it isn't pretty," you say.

"Steel," says Lou approvingly. "There's nothing better than steel."

The doctor looks up at you from under his smooth white eyebrows. You are still surprised to see that you are so much taller than he.

"Walk," he orders tersely.

With the crutches jammed firmly under your arms, you know exactly what to do. You step out firmly with your good right leg, then lift your left hip and swing forward Lou's handsome brace with its less important content of flesh and bone. You keep it up right down the hall, and, though your technique of foot travel might appear odd or even pitiful to the man on the street, you are terribly proud of it.

"Turn around," comes your next order from the doctor.

Thrusting your weight upon your good leg and one crutch, you pivot and come stepping and swinging yourself up the hall toward the little watchful group. You are grinning with all your might. You feel your neck muscles straining with the anxiety of this expression. You want the doctor's approval more than you have ever wanted anything in your life.

You reach the group and halt. The white head of the doctor is just below, bent down intently, as he stares at your legs. His hands, his quiet hands, which you have come to believe in as some people believe in God, reach out as he stoops, touching your good leg.

"You have done a fine job with this one," he says.

It is one of the few compliments he has ever paid you, and you feel your throat choking with happiness and pride.

He prods your weak leg, your shame, between the slender steel rods which give it strength. You both have worked very hard on that leg, and every tiny muscle failure in it is known perfectly to each of you.

"And don't give up this one," says the doctor. "There is something there. We don't know about it yet."

You feel each of his words dissolving into you. You wait. The doctor straightens. His blue eyes peer steadily into yours, the eyebrows lift intently.

"So you are going to Warm Springs," he says.

"Yes, this week, if you think I'm ready."

"Of course. Tomorrow, if you like."

You are grinning again, and the little crowd around you, nurses, physical therapists, murmur their congratulations. You have won the first big victory. You can walk alone. You can leave the hospital where you have suffered through the terrible beginning stages of the disease, and have climbed upward to the doorway, inch by inch.

You thank them all.

"Remember one thing," says the doctor quietly. He takes your arm above the elbow, and you are proud of the big clenching of muscle which you have developed with the exercises. "Remember, that you are just starting. Five months since the onset of polio. To you it seems a long time, but it is nothing. I think you will have some return of muscle strength for at least a year. You must keep working."

"And hoping, doctor?"

His eyes are deep on yours.

"Of course," he tells you.

He steps back.

You duck your head and try to keep on grinning. You feel his fingers gently pat your arm.

"All right, next patient," he says quickly, and you watch the group move away from you down the corridor.

Before going back to your wheel chair, you walk to each of the other beds in the big sunny room where you have spent a lifetime in five months.

"So you made it," says the pantie manufacturer, with a triumphant smile. You don't have to tell him, the look on your face is enough.

You nod. "Tomorrow. I can leave tomorrow."

He salutes you with his cigarette. "You miserable, miserable character," he says. "I'm going to miss you around here."

"Maybe you'll be next," you tell him. And then you are sorry you have said this. You all know that both legs and one arm are gone completely.

"Sure, I'll wriggle on my belly like a snake," he tells you.

The teen-age boy is gone from the next bed, and the new patient whom you scarcely know is deep in exhausted sleep. There is only the lawyer, your particular friend. You swing over to his bedside and stand there.

"It's terrific, the way you walk," he tells you proudly.

You know how it is with him. The weakness of one shoulder and arm have held him back from everything but the wheel chair and may for months to come.

"What a terrific right leg you've got there," he says.

You wish that you could give him a little of that strength, inject it into his shoulder.

You call for your wheel chair then, and sit down at his bedside. For nearly two hours you talk quietly. He is immensely happy about your success. It floods his thin, pain-worn face, softening it. You go over many of the small, terribly important experiences you have been through together. Then it is suppertime, then dark, and you hoist yourself into your high, narrow, white bed for the last time.

There is a full moon this night, and your bed is white and clear around you, blackness dropping depthlessly from its edges. It has been your home through the longest and deepest experience of your life. It has been the one sure thing in a totally dissolving world. You grip the thick edges of the mattress in your hands which have grown so strong. You lie for a long time without sleeping. In the morning you will walk back through the doorway into the firm world you knew, and you will make that passage without fear.

You relax, and the softness of the moonlight takes you gently into a dream in which your victory continues forever.